Understanding Complexity

Scott E. Page, Ph.D.

THE
GREAT
COURSES®

PUBLISHED BY:

THE GREAT COURSES
Corporate Headquarters
4840 Westfields Boulevard, Suite 500
Chantilly, Virginia 20151-2299
Phone: 1-800-832-2412
Fax: 703-378-3819
www.thegreatcourses.com

Scott E. Page, Ph.D.

Leonid Hurwicz Collegiate Professor
of Political Science, Complex Systems,
and Economics, University of Michigan
External Faculty Member, Santa Fe Institute

Professor Scott E. Page received a B.A. in Mathematics from the University of Michigan and an M.A. in Mathematics from the University of Wisconsin–Madison. He then received his M.S. in Business and his Ph.D. in Managerial Economics and Decision Sciences from the J. L. Kellogg School of Management at Northwestern University. He completed his Ph.D. thesis under the guidance of Stan Reiter and Nobel Laureate Roger Myerson. He has been a Professor of Economics at the Caltech and the University of Iowa and is currently Leonid Hurwicz Collegiate Professor of Political Science, Complex Systems, and Economics at the University of Michigan as well as a senior research scientist at the Institute for Social Research, a senior fellow in the Michigan Society of Fellows, and associate director of the Center for the Study of Complex Systems.

While a graduate student, Professor Page began visiting the Santa Fe Institute (SFI), an interdisciplinary think tank devoted to the study of complexity. He has been actively involved at SFI for more than 15 years. Currently, Professor Page serves as an external faculty member of SFI. For a dozen years, he, along with John Miller, has run a summer workshop for graduate students on computational modeling.

A popular advisor and instructor, Professor Page has won outstanding teaching assistant awards at the University of Wisconsin and Northwestern University, the Faculty Teaching Award at Caltech, and the Faculty Achievement Award for outstanding research, teaching, and service at the University of Michigan.

Professor Page's research interests span a wide range of disciplines. He has published papers in leading journals in economics, political science, ecology, physics, management, public health, and computer science. He has served on dissertation committees for students in more than 10 departments. In recent years, his core interest has been the various roles of diversity in complex adaptive systems, such as economies and ecosystems. He is the author of two books on these topics, *Complex Adaptive Systems* (with John Miller) and *The Difference: How the Power of Diversity Creates Better Firms, Groups, Schools, and Societies*. Both books were published by Princeton University Press.

Professor Page has spoken on complexity and diversity to many leading companies, universities, and nonprofit organizations, including the World Bank, the Kellogg Foundation, Yahoo!, and the National Academies. He lives with his wife and two sons in Ann Arbor, Michigan. ■

Table of Contents

Table of Contents

Understanding Complexity

Scope:

Complexity science has become a phenomenon. Newspapers, magazines, and books introducing the core concepts from complexity science (emergence, tipping points, the wisdom of crowds, power laws, scale-free networks, and six degrees of separation, to name just a few) have flooded the mainstream. This popularization has taken place at the same time that complex systems techniques have gained a foothold in the academy. The analyses of political systems, economies, ecologies, and epidemics increasingly invoke concepts and techniques from complexity science.

In this course, we learn the nuts and bolts of complexity. We cover the core concepts and ideas that have transformed complexity from a loose collection of metaphorical intuitions into a respected scientific discipline in less than a quarter century. The science of complexity contains a plethora of models and ideas through which we can interpret and understand the world around us. Thus we keep an eye on reality throughout, touching on the practical benefits of gaining an understanding of complex systems.

We begin by defining complexity, which proves to be rather challenging. Many people confuse complexity with chaos, difficulty, or complicatedness; it's none of the three. We'll see that different disciplines rely on distinct conceptions and measures of complexity. What a computer scientist and an ecologist call complexity do not align perfectly, but the definitions will be close enough for us to get some leverage.

One of our goals will be to see complexity science in a transdisciplinary light, as a set of ideas, concepts, and tools that can be applied across disciplines. Hence in the lectures that follow, we flow in and out of traditional disciplinary boundaries. We will discuss the spread of diseases, the collapse of ecosystems, and the growth of the Internet. Sometimes we will link concepts tightly to specific real-world situations. Other times we will paint with a broad brush and discuss how a core concept transcends boundaries.

One of those transcendent ideas is the notion of emergence. Emergent macro-level properties arise through the interaction of lower-level entities and often bear no resemblance to them. The wetness of water is an emergent property, as is a heartbeat. We also discuss how in some cases, interactions produce critical states, in which small events can produce cascading changes. This process of self-organized criticality has been offered as an explanation for widespread power outages, stock market crashes, and traffic jams. Self-organized criticality is just one way in which small events can produce large disruptions. Systems can tip from one absorbing state to another. We'll learn why and how.

By definition, the topic of complexity is, well, complex. We cannot get around that. Throughout the course, we'll balance the need for precise understanding against the necessity of technical concepts. Jargon will be outlawed. The guiding principles for these lectures will be to move beyond metaphor (a butterfly flapping its wings) and anecdote (someone buying a pair of Hush Puppies) to a deeper, logical understanding of core concepts. Among the questions we take up: What is path dependence? What is a power law? How do you explain the phenomenon of six degrees of separation? What really is a tipping point? In addition, we'll learn to apply complex systems thinking to our personal and professional lives. Along the way, we'll have loads of fun! ∎

Complexity—What Is It? Why Does It Matter?

Lecture 1

What are complex systems? What is complexity? ... And why does it matter?

In everyday life, the word "complex" might be applied to our lives, the economy, or even salad dressing. Our first step in constructing a science of complexity will be to construct definitions and measures. A system will be said to be complex if the whole transcends the parts. Most complex systems consist of diverse entities that interact both in space (either real or virtual) and in time. Most ecosystems, New York City, and an elementary school playground each satisfy this definition of complex, but a window air conditioner does not. Addressing many of our most pressing challenges—such as managing ecosystems and economies, or preventing mass epidemics and market crashes—will require understanding the functioning of complex systems.

When we describe something as complex, we mean that it consists of interdependent, diverse entities, and we assume that those entities adapt—that they respond to their local and global environments. Complex systems interest us for several reasons. They are often unpredictable, they can produce large events, and they can withstand substantial trauma. Complex systems produce bottom-up emergent phenomena, where what occurs on the macro level differs in kind from what we see in the parts. Emergence takes many forms, including self-organization. Finally, complex systems produce amazing novelty, from sea slugs to laser printers.

From a pragmatic perspective, our world forces us to take an interest in complexity. How do we make sense of it? In this course, we will formulate a reasonably precise definition of complexity so that we can accurately compare the complexity of situations. We will learn about complexity theory, a new way of thinking with new computational tools. We will move beyond metaphor and introduce the science and vocabulary of complex systems. A complex system is capable of producing structures and patterns from the bottom up. It does not settle into a simple pattern but instead is a source of near-perpetual novelty. It is not in equilibrium, nor is it chaotic.

A system can be considered complex if its agents meet four qualifications: diversity, connection, interdependence, and adaptation. Rather than just saying "economies are complex" or "ecosystems are complex," we can now base those statements on logical foundations. These four qualifications can also be used to prove that the world is becoming more complex by almost any measure: social, economic, political, physical, ecological, or biological. In addition, science has given us finer lenses with which to recognize complexity.

Our world forces us to take an interest in complexity.

At this point, we need to make an important distinction: Complex is not the same thing as complicated. Complicated systems may have diverse parts, but they are not adaptive. In addition to adaptability and robustness, complex systems have the ability to produce large events. Because they can produce large events, complex systems are often said to be not normal, or outside of the common distribution curve. It may seem paradoxical that complex systems are both robust and subject to large events, yet it is not.

Many people, including myself, study complex systems because of the mystery of emergence. Emergence is when the macro differs from the micro—not just in scale but in kind. One common form of emergence is self-organization. This occurs when a spatial pattern or structure emerges, such as flocks of birds or schools of fish. One fascinating thing about emergent phenomena is that they arise from the bottom up, without superimposed formalism.

Complex systems produce interesting dynamics such as phase transitions, which are sometimes called tipping points. Phase transitions occur when forces within a system reach what is called the critical threshold. Once this happens, the state of the system changes, often drastically. A phase transition is a type of nonlinearity. Unfortunately, there are many ways to be nonlinear. ■

Suggested Reading

Ball, *Critical Mass*.

Miller and Page, *Complex Adaptive Systems*.

Resnick, *Turtles, Termites, and Traffic Jams*.

Questions to Consider

1. How might you make more formal a claim that financial markets or international politics have become more complex?

2. Is making a situation less complex necessarily better?

Simple, Rugged, and Dancing Landscapes
Lecture 2

> Dancing landscapes are complex. ... Figuring out what to do in a complex situation isn't easy; and even if you do figure it out, what was a good idea today may not be a good idea tomorrow.

In this lecture, we will use the idea of a landscape both as a metaphor and as a mathematical object. The simplest landscapes resemble Mount Fuji, which is shaped like a giant pyramid. Most of the landscapes that we will talk about will have many more peaks and valleys, much like the Appalachian Mountains. These are called rugged landscapes. People often conflate complex systems with rugged landscapes, but that is not quite right. The qualities of interdependence and adaptability in complex systems create landscapes that are not just rugged but dancing.

These three categories of landscape—simple (Mount Fuji), rugged, and dancing—are the main themes of this lecture. We will use these categories to understand why some problems can be solved optimally and some cannot. We will use the idea of a landscape to lay the foundation for how we will think about complexity. We will not just use the landscape as a metaphor. We will also have a formal, mathematical definition of a landscape.

Before we start, we need to define the two types of peak: local and global. A local peak is a place on the landscape from which a step in any direction is a step down in elevation. A global peak is the highest of all of the local peaks of a given landscape. Most of the time the global peak is unique. Mount Fuji landscapes are single peaked; the local and global peak are by definition one and the same. Rugged landscapes have many local peaks, and it sometimes can be difficult to find the global peak. Dancing landscapes can have a single peak or multiple peaks, but the key feature is that those peaks change over time.

In complex systems, agents adapt locally. If performance is considered as elevate on, then we can think of these agents as climbing hills. The local peaks are the best nearby options, whereas the global peaks are the best possible actions.

We will start by looking at the Mount Fuji landscape in the context of a real-world problem. The insight that experimentation can locate better solutions underpinned an approach to business that was pioneered by Fredrick Taylor in the early 1990s. It is often called Taylorism in his honor. Taylor solved a famous design problem involving the optimal size of a shovel. When charting the productivity of a shovel at increasing sizes on a topographical map, we find that it results in a two-dimensional Mount Fuji landscape. Since it is very easy to find the global peak in a Mount Fuji landscape, the productivity of an economy based on physical labor is easy to optimize by using scientific management.

At the turn of the 20th century, most problems were handled with manual labor on singular tasks, such as laying rails.

The world of Taylor is not the world of today. The world of today involves more rugged and dancing landscapes. Finding the highest point on a rugged landscape is not easy. The main reason is that the space of possibilities can be combinatorially huge. However, a large range of combinations is not the only thing necessary for a rugged landscape; the ingredients also have to interact. Once they do, the landscapes begin to have local peaks. These interactions occur within the choices of a single agent, as we can see when we consider the chain of effects created from the decision to remodel one aspect of a house. The simple rule is that the more interactions occur, the more rugged the landscape.

As difficult as rugged problems can be, they are not complex. To get complexity, we need to make the landscape dance. To explain the difference between a rugged landscape and a dancing landscape, we will look at two problems, one involving a milk distributor and one involving an airline. The problem of the milk distributor is difficult but remains fixed. The problem of the airline, however, contains multiple and interdependent actors; therefore, it dances. The difference is subtle. Interactions between our own choices are what make a landscape rugged. Interdependencies between our actions and the actions of others are what make a landscape dance. Interdependencies only come into play if the actors adapt. Hence complexity requires both interdependence

Let's do a quick summary of what we have learned about landscapes so far. We can think of the value of a potential solution to a problem as its elevation, so we can therefore think of a problem as creating a landscape. When a problem is simple, with no interactions, we get a Mount Fuji landscape. When our choices interact, we have a rugged landscape. If the elevations depend on the actions of others, and these actors exhibit interdependency and adaptation, then we have a dancing landscape.

In complex systems, agents adapt locally.

Why do all of these landscapes matter? Seeing the distinction between a Mount Fuji landscape and a rugged landscape helps us to understand why evolutionary and creative systems sometimes can find an optimal solution and sometimes cannot. The distinction between fixed and dancing landscapes has implications for how we allocate resources. Rugged landscapes have a good chance of repaying investment, whereas dancing landscapes do not.

The final and most intriguing insight that comes from these landscape models relates to what is called a standpoint, or perspective. In creative systems, there is no landscape. The landscape is determined by the way a problem is encoded. If a problem were encoded according to certain attributes, then the landscape might be simple. If the same problem were encoded according to other attributes, it might be rugged. The same logic holds for complex situations—how we encode them influences how quickly and effectively we can adapt. ■

Suggested Reading

Holland, *Adaptation in Natural and Artificial Systems*.

Mitchell, *An Introduction to Genetic Algorithms*.

Page, *The Difference*.

Questions to Consider

1. How have changes in technology made the landscapes facing firms, organizations, and governments more rugged?

2. Why might we commit fewer resources to formulating a policy on a dancing landscape then we would for a fixed, rugged landscape?

The Interesting In-Between
Lecture 3

To dig more deeply into how the attributes of interdependence, connectedness, diversity, and adaptation and learning generate complexity, we can imagine that each of these attributes is a dial that can be turned from 0 (lowest) to 10 (highest).

We are going to spend this lecture twisting those dials to see which combinations lead to complexity and which do not. Contrary to what we might expect, we will not get complexity at the extremes. Complexity exists in a region that I like to call the interesting in-between. First, we need to come to a common understanding of what behaviors a system might take on. For that, we need to categorize both the system and its initial states. The behavior of a system can depend on its state and the rules followed by its parts.

Physicist Stephen Wolfram divides the behaviors of systems into four classes. Class 1 behaviors are stable, single-point equilibria, like a ball at rest at the bottom of a bowl. This behavior is said to be resistant to perturbation. Class 2 behaviors are called periodic orbits. A periodic orbit is a regular sequence of states, like the cycle of a stoplight. Class 3 behaviors are chaotic, meaning that they are extremely sensitive to initial conditions. An example of this would be the proverbial butterfly that flaps its wings and creates a hurricane. Class 4 behaviors are complex. They have regular structure but they also have high information content, meaning that they would take a long time to describe. What has to be true about a system for it to fall into one of these four classes? Experiments with our dials will show us.

Let's start with the interdependency dial. With the interdependency dial set at 0, each person does what he or she wants to without any concern about what others do. Think of a person choosing to wear a sweater when it is cold. If we ramp up the interdependency to a moderate level, as in a teenager trying to decide on a cool sweater to wear, we get complexity. If we turn the interdependency dial up higher, so that the teenager is trying to gauge the coolness not just of the sweater but of every item of clothing, we get a chaotic mess. One student changing his initial outfit could result in a drastically different path of outfits for all students. It will not always be the case that high interdependency leads to chaos. Sometimes it just causes an incomprehensible mangle.

The next dial is connectedness. Whereas interdependence refers to whether other entities influence actions, connectedness refers to how many people a person is connected to. If a person is completely disconnected from everyone else, no one else can have any effect on that person's actions. The result is not complex. If we hold the interdependency at a moderate level and raise the level of connectedness, we come up with some interesting results. We can see this in the greeting game, in which people "best respond," meaning that they respond in the way they remember their connections responding before. At a somewhat low level of connectedness, equilibrium is established rather quickly. At a moderate level of connectedness, it can take a long while for equilibrium to be achieved. At a high level of connectedness, equilibrium is once again achieved quickly.

The same phenomenon exists if the game is made more complicated, as in rock-paper-scissors. Although in this game the best-response technique is used to mismatch others instead of match them, complexity is still only found in situations of moderate connectedness. If we apply the same experiment to the *Escherichia coli* found in our bodies, we find a real-life rock-paper-scissors game in which the states can be labeled sensitive, toxic, and resistant. Almost all games studied in game theory have either two players or infinite players. As a result, game theory tends to ignore the interesting in-between, where complexity happens.

Almost all games studied in game theory have either two players or infinite players. As a result, game theory tends to ignore the interesting in-between, where complexity happens.

We move on to diversity. When we say diversity, we mean differences in types. We do not mean variations. If we take chemical elements as our different types and we adjust them from no diversity to moderate diversity to high diversity, we find the same pattern as in interdependence and connectedness: from simple to complex to a mess. The same thing holds for ecosystems, with the exception that a high diversity of species can sustain complexity if interactions with other species are restricted, as is the case with niches. In most cases, however, high diversity leads to the collapse of the ecosystem.

We are now ready to study the relationship between complexity and adaptation and learning. We should think of this dial not as increasing the speed with which entities adapt but as increasing the intelligence of these entities. If there is no adaptation or learning, simple parts follow fixed rules and remain in equilibrium. A little learning or adaptation goes a long way. It allows the parts to figure out how to interact with one another to create a coherent, complex whole. When we turn the learning dial all the way up, we often get equilibrium again. If everyone is optimizing relative to what everyone else is doing, there is no need for the system to change, and we get what is called in game theory a Nash equilibrium.

When we say a system is complex, we mean that it produces interesting nonperiodic patterns and emergent structures and functionalities. We have found that this complex state tends to lie in a region of moderate interdependence, moderate connectedness, some diversity, and some adaptation. Implicit in what we have learned is an explanation for why we see so much complexity in the social world. As social beings, we are connected, interdependent, diverse, and smart—but all in moderation. ■

Suggested Reading

West, *Scaling Laws in Biology and Other Complex Systems*.

Questions to Consider

1. In a complex system, does increasing the number of connections have the same effect as increasing interdependencies?

2. If government becomes an incomprehensible mangle, how might it respond to regain vibrancy? Alternatively, if the same government became predictable and ineffectual, how might it achieve vibrancy?

Why Different Is More
Lecture 4

With just two distinct bits—a zero and a one—and enough time, we can produce all the differences that have ever been and that ever can be.

We now focus on the role of difference—either variation in type or diversity of type—in complex systems. It is important to realize that a population that is referred to as a unified whole can differ genetically and phenotypically. This variation within a population allows adaptation. Before we can talk about diversity, we have to know what it is. Over the past half-century, statisticians, ecologists, computer scientists, and economists have proposed a variety of diversity measures.

We can distinguish between four types of diversity measures: variation measures, entropy measures, distance measures, and attribute-based measures. Measures can either be constructed from the ground up by experimenting with mathematical formulae, or they can be derived analytically from a list of desiderata. Diversity measures compress information. They transform sets of diverse entities into single numbers. In the process, meaningful distinctions disappear. Because diversity measures can be applied to a variety of entities, and because each of these sets has distinct properties, we should not expect a one-size-fits-all measure.

The great inventor Thomas Edison experimented with combinations.

Variation measures capture differences along a single numerical attribute. We capture that variation by means of a distribution, which plots the range of values and their likelihood. The most common measures of this type are statistical variance and its square root, standard deviation. To take into account different types, we need an entropy measure. Entropy measures capture the evenness of a distribution across types. Entropy measures depend on the number of types. The more types, the more entropy. The flaw with entropy measures is that they do not take type-level differences into account.

Two types of measure have been constructed that do take type-level differences into account: distance measures and attribute measures. Distance measures assume a preexisting distance function for pairs of types—for instance, genetic distance in the case of species. Attribute measures identify the attributes of each type in the set and then count up the total number of unique attributes. There are four causes of diversity in complex systems. Perhaps the biggest cause of diversity is diversity itself. The more diversity you start with, the more you can produce. The second cause of diversity is weak selective pressure. If there is no selective pressure, nothing stops diversity from spreading. Another cause of diversity is different landscapes. In this case, the diversity arises because the problems that need to be solved are different, so the peaks differ. The final way in which selection can produce type diversity is through dancing landscapes, where movements on one landscape shift the heights on other landscapes.

Diversity measures compress information. ... In the process, meaningful distinctions disappear.

Can we say anything about how systems in which diversity evolves, like ecosystems, differ from systems in which diversity is created by purposeful actors? Let's look at a few key differences. The first difference relates to the size of the leaps. Evolution is a plodder, but creative systems can take big leaps. The second difference relates to interim viability. Evolution is constrained in that each step along the path to an improvement must be viable. Creative processes do not have this constraint. The third difference relates to representation. Evolution is stuck with genetic representations. It cannot switch to some new encoding. This is not true for creative systems. ■

Suggested Reading

Page, *The Difference*.

Weiner, *The Beak of the Finch*.

Questions to Consider

1. Suppose that you run a research-based organization. How might you know if you have too little or too much diversity among your researchers?

2. Can you think of an example of where less variation would be better? Does this example contradict what we learned in this lecture?

Explore Exploit—The Fundamental Trade-Off
Lecture 5

A complex system consists of these little entities that have interdependent payoffs and rules that create emergent phenomena, robustness, and possibly large events.

A fundamental trade-off in a complex system is exploration versus exploitation. By exploration, we mean searching for better solutions. By exploitation, we mean taking advantage of what you know—reaping the benefits of past searches. Ideally, exploration should be balanced against exploitation. Why must actors in a complex system maintain this balance, and how does doing so help maintain complexity? We begin by describing the explore/exploit trade-off in the context of a decision problem called the two-armed bandit problem. We see how the explore/exploit trade-off manifests itself in rugged and dancing landscapes. We discuss an algorithm for balancing exploration with exploitation called simulated annealing. We then turn to evolutionary systems and see how the basic mechanisms of evolution can be seen through the prism of the explore/exploit trade-off.

The two-armed bandit problem. Imagine a slot machine with two levers, one on the right and one on the left. The levers offer the same payout but at a different rate. The problem is how to balance exploration (testing the rates of both levers) and exploitation (acting on a determination based on previous testing) to maximize return.

We return to the concept of a rugged landscape and describe how exploration and exploitation play out there. Recall the hiker whose ambition is to find a point of high elevation. This hiker has limited time and wants to spend as much of it as possible on high ground. Using the rule that he only proceeds with each step if it takes him higher, the hiker would very quickly reach the summit of a Mount Fuji landscape. However, this rule would perform poorly in a rugged landscape. Computer scientists refer to this sort of search rule as a greedy algorithm.

A much better alternative would be the search approach known as simulated annealing. We study simulated annealing for three reasons. It works. It provides a segue into the concept of self-organization. It shows the fan-out nature of complex systems. First of all, what is annealing? Annealing is used to harden glass and metals and to make crystals. Spin glass is a stylized model of glass, metal, or crystal. It is an enormous checkerboard of particles, each with a spin (either pointed up or down). The goal is to get all of these particles to point in the same direction.

Glassmakers and metallurgists use annealing to accomplish this. Annealing takes advantage of the fact that particles want to line up with their neighbors, much like magnets. When the metal is too cold, the particles are frozen in what physicists call a frustrated or disorganized state. The trick seems to be to heat the metal until the particles are free to move; but if we keep the heat on high, the particles will never settle down. If we heat the metal just enough so that the particles can move, they will align with their neighbors, but not all local neighborhoods will agree. The result will be a camouflage pattern. Once the camouflage pattern forms, we cool the temperature a bit to achieve what is called annealing. The boundaries of the neighborhoods shift back and forth until by chance the regions absorb one another and become uniform. Once this is achieved, the temperature is cooled further so that the system freezes in an organized state.

Natural selection is a form of exploitation, resulting in genetic fitness.

Let's go back to our hiker and apply a simulated annealing algorithm to his searches. Think of temperature as a proxy for the probability of making a mistake. If the temperature is high, lots of mistakes are made; if very low, none. In this model, a higher temperature means more exploring, and a lower temperature means more exploiting. When we put our hiker in a rugged landscape, the temperature starts high—he just explores a lot. As we cool the temperature, the hiker becomes more likely to go up than down. When the temperature becomes very cool, he inevitably ends up on a local peak. While this may not provide the optimum solution, it does provide a good one. Optimal cooling depends on the ruggedness of the landscape.

Evolution balances exploration and exploitation. Mutation and recombination of genes are forms of exploration, resulting in genetic diversity. Natural selection is a form of exploitation, resulting in genetic fitness. Although this is a gross simplification, it is a useful one.

Let's now turn to dancing landscapes—in particular, the complex system of leafcutter ants. Leafcutter ant colonies are massive productive systems, with ants of various sizes each suited to a different task. How is this a dancing landscape? The fungi the ants produce attract bacteria, which threaten to overwhelm the ants. The ants have an antibiotic system consisting of different bacteria that grow on their backs, which attack the invading bacteria. This shows a constant balance between exploration and exploitation. The leafcutter ants had to form a relationship with the bacteria in order to maintain elevation on the dancing landscape.

Therefore, rugged and dancing landscapes require different explore/exploit balances. We saw how on a rugged landscape the balance between exploration and exploitation should end with almost complete exploitation. Hence we devise algorithms like simulated annealing, which start out exploring but end up exploiting. On dancing landscapes, agents can never stop exploring. This explains why we see complexity: Equilibrium allows for exploration, which stimulates dancing landscapes. Randomness is avoided because as exploration becomes prevalent, the value of exploitation increases. Thus individual agents balance the necessity to explore and exploit, producing complexity as a result. Complexity can thus be thought of as an emergent property. ■

Suggested Reading

Kauffman, *At Home in the Universe*.

1. What do you make of the following claim? "Organizations that attempt to turn dancing landscapes into rugged landscapes ultimately fail."

2. How might an organization apply the concept of simulated annealing into its standard operating procedure for developing new policies? Recall that the temperature can be thought of as the probability of making a mistake.

Emergence I—Why More Is Different
Lecture 6

Systems with many parts can produce emergent phenomena that cannot be true of the parts themselves. A pool of water can be wet, but a single water molecule cannot. Differentiated cells can combine to form a heart, a lung, or a whole person. Interconnected neurons can produce consciousness. How?

In this lecture, we discuss one of the most fascinating ideas from complex systems: emergence. Emergence refers to the spontaneous creation of order and functionality from the bottom up. If we look at the physical world, we see emergent patterns at every level, from galaxies to cells. Not only do we see structure in the physical world, we also see functionality. All of this happens without a central planner. It emerges from the bottom up. Before getting into the scientific details of emergence, I am going to describe in some detail a particular emergent phenomenon: slime molds.

Slime molds are amoebalike single-celled organisms that feed on decaying plant and vegetable matter. Slime molds only become interesting when under stress, and by stress I mean a lack of food. When this happens, an individual bit of slime will secrete an enzyme as a type of warning signal. This prompts other bits of slime to secrete the enzyme as well. The enzymes create a path, and the bits of mold begin to gather in a colony called a pseudoplasmodium. Though it has no brain or heart, the pseudoplasmodium begins to travel. At some point, the colony stops moving and begins to pile on top of itself to form a stalk. The individuals that make it to the top of the stalk release mold spores that spread by wind or rain. Although they started out as identical, the individuals now perform different tasks, a process known as breaking symmetry. This is epic emergence. Individual parts bind together to create a way to survive. As amazing as slime mold is, it is nothing compared to the human brain. Consciousness is, in many respects, the ultimate emergence.

We now turn to the science of emergence. We will talk through the various definitions and types of emergence and how they occur. There are two different distinctions between types of emergence: simple versus complex and strong versus weak. Simple emergence is a macro-level property in an equilibrium system, like the wetness created by weak hydrogen bonds holding together water molecules. Complex emergence is also a macro-level property, but it exists in a complex system not in equilibrium, like the mobility of slime molds. Strong emergence says that whatever occurs at the macro level cannot be deduced from interactions at the micro level. Weak emergence says that whatever occurs at the macro level would not be expected from interactions at the micro level.

To see how emergence arises, let's consider a model borrowed from Stephen Wolfram, called the one-dimensional cellular automaton. Three light bulbs are arranged in a triangle, each with two possible states: on or off. If a simple rule is applied to the model, blinking emerges as a property of the system. A similar process occurs in the biological world in the blinking pattern of fireflies. The fact that a rule applied locally leads to a macro-level property is what is meant by the term bottom up.

Consistency allows people to figure out what to do when new domains arise.

We now move from the blinking of fireflies to the formation of culture. In each case, we get coordinated behavior at the macro level that arises through micro-level interdependencies. We define culture as a set of shared beliefs, behaviors, and routines. Let's assume that there are 100 domains in which beliefs or actions are interdependent. For each domain, we will assume that people play a pure coordination game, in which a positive payoff occurs when people do the same thing. If we send people to interact within the domain, eventually the entire population coordinates their actions.

This model does not explain the fact that cultures have meaning and coherence. To account for this, we need to include interactions between the various domains. We need to make the landscape rugged. To do this, we will assume that people also value consistency. Consistency allows people to figure out what to do when new domains arise. Our full model then is one in which people walk around and interact. They coordinate and strive for consistency. What emerges? Something that looks a lot like culture. Cultures exhibit emergent functionalities. They allow people to know how others will behave. People know how to behave in novel situations.

Blinking fireflies and emergent cultures are interesting, but they are a long way from consciousness or emotion. For now, let's move to a model that produces an emergent functionality: robustness. Imagine a row of banks that have relationships with one another—they each have callable deposits that they can withdraw from their neighbors. Each bank has a choice: to make risky loans or safe loans. The risky loans pay more, but they may make other banks nervous enough to call back their deposits. We are going to let our banks learn whether to make risky loans or safe loans. Most will begin by making risky loans, but some will see the value of making safe loans. Those that choose to make safe loans will be breaking the symmetry of the original model. Soon, a pattern emerges: three or four risky banks, one safe bank (repeating). The emergent functionality that this pattern produces is a firewall, which makes the entire system robust. Does this mean that we should allow systems to evolve and that eventually robust outcomes will emerge from the bottom up? Not necessarily. ∎

Suggested Reading

Anderson, "More is Different."

Beinhocker, *Origin of Wealth*, chap. 6.

Holland, *Emergence*.

Miller and Page, *Complex Adaptive Systems*.

Newman, "Power Laws, Pareto Distributions, and Zipf's Law."

Questions to Consider

1. Can you think of a rule birds might use to form a flock or one fish might use to form a school?

2. Do you think the human heartbeat is strongly emergent or weakly emergent? Is it a form of simple emergence or is it complex emergence?

Emergence II—Network Structure and Function
Lecture 7

Our physical life takes place in geographic space, but the worlds of commerce and ideas take place in both physical and virtual space.

In this lecture, we discuss networks and how they matter for complex systems. Over the last 20 years, network theory has burst into the mainstream. Networks, and space more generally, are central concepts within complex systems. In complex systems, space matters; the connections between people, ideas, and species influence how events play out. Models used in textbooks and taught in universities often leave space out. There are two reasons for this. Good modeling requires simplification. Networks and space were once thought to be superfluous. Networks were thought to be too difficult to model. There have been recent breakthroughs; we have new models of networks, and we have agent-based models. In some cases, networks do not matter, and in others they do, as can be seen in the spread of disease.

Complex systems models take spacing seriously. We start with some basic terminology and measures of networks. We talk about some common network structures. We discuss how those networks came to be. Finally, we discuss some properties of these various networks.

Let's start with some basics of networks. A network consists of nodes and edges. Nodes are things, and edges are relationships or connections. A network is said to be connected if you can get from one node to another. We can construct some measures of the system that tell us something about it. We can calculate the degree of each node, meaning the number of edges connected to it. We can compute the path length, or distance, between two nodes. This is the minimum number of edges that you have to move along to get from one node to another. Averages can be computed for both degrees and path lengths in a system. We can explore the properties of these measurements by using the United States as our model, where each state is a node and each border is an edge. We can compare this to a hub-and-spokes network, like those that airline and delivery companies have developed. The hub-and-spokes network is top down, but we want to talk about emergent networks. We will start with something called the random connection model. The result is something akin to the six degrees of separation experiment. These networks are fun, but let's turn to something more important: social networks.

Social networks are not random, in that your friends are also likely to be friends with each other. This is known in network theory as clustering. How, if social networks are clustered, can they also exhibit the low average path length seen in the six degrees of separation phenomenon? The solution lies in something called a small-worlds network. I have my close-knit friends, called clique friends. In addition, I have friends I have met incidentally, called random friends. A small-worlds network consists of lots of clique friends and some random friends. This network has a low average path length; the random friends extend our connections.

Social networks are not random, in that your friends are also likely to be friends with each other. This is known in network theory as clustering.

What is the structure of the World Wide Web? It is neither a random network nor a small-worlds network. It is what we call a power-law network. We call it this because the distribution of the degrees of nodes satisfies a power law. Power-law distributions have lots of nodes with very low degree and a few nodes with very high degree. If we had a huge graph with a million nodes with degree 1, it would have 250,000 nodes with degree 2, 10,000 with degree 10, and 100 with degree 100. This is called long-tailed distribution.

In each of the cases we have seen, structure emerges. This raises the question: How do these structures emerge? Are they weakly emergent or strongly emergent? The answer is that they are weakly emergent. To understand why, we construct a model. We assign people various attributes and allow them to interact. People will tend to hang out with people like themselves, forming cliques. Random connections come from the fact that people have friends and relatives in different locations. This explains small-worlds networks, but power-law networks are more difficult to explain. For this, we use what is called a preferential attachment model. We use the World Wide Web as an example. When a new website appears, it wants to connect to websites with the most links. This seems to give preference to those websites that were created earliest. However, some of the most popular sites were latecomers. Therefore, the model was amended to allow sites also to have quality. Higher-quality sites exhibited attractions as well as higher-volume sites. This extended model generates an emergent long-tailed distribution.

Now we want to talk about a different property of networks (and also a general property of complex systems): robustness. We say that connectedness is the ability to get from any node to any other node. In terms of the Internet or power grids, connectedness is central. To determine the robustness of a network, we can perform knockout experiments. In a knockout experiment, we remove nodes and ask if the network remains connected. If we randomly knock out a few nodes in a power-law network, chances are that the network will remain connected. If we strategically knock out the highly connected nodes, the network will fail. Therefore, a power-law network is very susceptible to strategic attack. This does not mean that the network is in a critical state where large events are to be expected. We should see networks themselves as complex systems with diverse interacting adaptive components. ■

Suggested Reading

Epstein, *Generative Social Science.*

Jackson, *Social and Economic Networks.*

Newman, Barabasi, and Watts, *The Structure and Dynamics of Networks.*

Watts, *Six Degrees of Separation.*

1. Try to connect yourself to the president of the United States in a path length of 6 or less. If you succeed, see if you can connect to Elvis in less than seven steps.

2. Think through whether a small-worlds network would be robust (i.e., whether it would stay connected) if you had a random or strategic knockout of nodes.

Agent-Based Modeling—The New Tool
Lecture 8

Agent-based modeling ... [has] been driving a lot of research in complex systems. Agent-based models are computer models that enable us to explore complex systems in greater detail.

In this lecture, we are going to talk about a new methodology: agent-based modeling. Agent-based models are computer models that enable us to explore complex systems. First, we talk about Philo T. Farnsworth. At the age of 14, Farnsworth thought of using lines of light on a cathode ray tube to project images sent through airwaves. In other words, he thought up the idea of television. According to legend, he got this idea from plowing lines in a field on his farm. Why are we talking about this story? To demonstrate how scientific breakthroughs such as these depend in equal parts on new ideas (the horizontal lines) and new tools (the cathode ray tube). In some cases, ideas drive the development of tools. Other times, we develop the tools first. New tools create opportunities, or they reveal information or a structure, which then results in new theories or substantiates old ones. So is the science of complex systems being driven by tools or by ideas? The answer is a little bit of both.

What is an agent-based model? Rick Riolo, a leading producer of agent-based models, describes them as consisting of entities of various types (the so-called agents) who are endowed with limited memory and cognitive ability, display interdependent behaviors, and are embedded in a network. A key assumption will be that the agents follow rules. Nowadays, the rules are written in computer code, and the behavior of the models can be watched on a computer screen. The rules that agents follow can be simple and fixed, or they can be sophisticated and adaptive.

In many agent-based models, the agents take discrete actions—they decide to move locations, switch from being cooperative to defecting, or change whether to join or exit a particular activity. Because of that, the rules they follow are threshold-based. "Threshold-based" means that the agent's behavior remains the same unless some threshold is met. Once that threshold is passed, the agent changes its behavior. These threshold effects can produce either positive or negative feedback.

Let's start with a simple agent-based model: John Horton Conway's *Game of Life*. Imagine an enormous checkerboard. Each square on this checkerboard contains an agent. That agent is in one of two states: alive or dead. Time in this model moves in discrete steps. So there is time period 0, time period 1, time period 2, and so on. In each period, each agent follows a fixed rule. The rule depends on what is happening in the eight cells surrounding the agent. Hence their behaviors are interdependent. With a simple rule, we get a blinking pattern much like we saw with the cellular automaton. What differs in this case is that the rules seem disconnected from the blinking.

Ideally, a modeling approach would have the logical consistency of equation-based models and the flexibility of verbal stories.

Agent-based models allow us to write the rules of the *Game of Life* in a computer program and to think of each cell as an individual agent. We can then start the program in a figure eight and see what emerges. What emerges, astoundingly, is a periodic orbit. That orbit happens to be of length 8. After eight periods of following the rules of the *Game of Life*, the system returns to its original configuration. In the game, it is possible to create gliders. These are configurations that reproduce themselves like the figure eight but do so one square to the left or right (or up or down). Not only does the game support gliders, it also supports glider guns. These are pulsing collections of cells that spit out gliders at regular intervals. The *Game of Life* has been proven to be capable of universal computation. Anything a computer can do, the *Game of Life* can do.

Agent-based models are also capable of what we might call high-fidelity modeling. Let's consider two such models, both dealing with potentially horrific events: fires in crowded buildings and epidemics. Imagine you are a building inspector and that you have to decide how many people can be allowed in a room. Consider two rooms, both 1,600 square feet. The first is 80 feet by 20 feet and has two doors on one of the 20-foot ends. The second room is 40 feet by 40 feet (a square) and has two doors in the middle of one side. We want to ask which room is easier to evacuate. We pull out a laptop and we write a computer program with three parts: the room, the people, and the fire. The room can be thought of as the environment, the people as the agents, and the fire as an event. In the rectangular room, our agents run toward the door, forming a line, and as a result they flow out relatively smoothly. The square room creates pileups and potential disasters. How could we prevent such disasters? We cannot make all square rooms rectangular. We can find alternatives through agent-based modeling.

One of the great concerns in modern society is the potential spread of an epidemic. How can agent-based models help us understand this process? It is possible to create an elaborate model—include every airline flight and every passenger who may or may not carry disease. We can then do experiments, such as seeing what happens if we shut down an airport. We can also understand how seemingly unimportant differences in transportation architecture could play large roles in disease spread.

All complex models can be constructed as agent-based models. What do we get out of them? What is the purpose of a model? Some people believe that the goal is to use the model to make predictions that can be empirically falsified. We can also use models to explore. We can also use models to run counterfactuals. Without agent-based models, we have two choices. We can write down a stark mathematical equation–based model, such as is used in basic economics courses or in a systems dynamics course. These are logically consistent but stark. The other alternative would be to construct a narrative, or story, of how we think events will unfold. The story has an advantage in that it is flexible. The cost of that flexibility is a potential lack of logical consistency. Ideally, a modeling approach would have the logical consistency of equation-based models and the flexibility of verbal stories. Agent-based models have both of those qualities. Constructing a complete model is often as valuable a learning experience as seeing what the model spits out. ■

Suggested Reading

Axelrod, *The Complexity of Cooperation*.

Epstein, *Growing Artificial Societies*.

Miller and Page, *Complex Adaptive Systems*.

Resnick, *Turtles, Termites, and Traffic Jams*.

Questions to Consider

1. Start with four live cells in a row, and then describe the next three periods in Conway's *Game of Life*.

2. In *Complex Adaptive Systems*, Miller and Page describe some agent-based models of a standing ovations. Try to construct your own model.

Feedbacks—Beehives, QWERTY, the Big Sort
Lecture 9

We're going to focus on feedbacks: positive feedbacks, in which more creates more; and negative feedbacks, in which more creates less.

In this lecture, we drill deeper into the implications of interdependent behaviors. We see how positive feedback creates tipping phenomena. We see how negative feedback creates stability. We see how combinations of negative and positive feedback produce path dependence. We also cover externalities. Let's get down some basic definitions. Actions that create positive feedback produce more of the same actions. In contrast, actions that create negative feedback produce less of the same actions. In complex systems models (and in the real world), agents use threshold-based rules. For an agent to act, some variable must be above or below a threshold. There is a subtle distinction between feedback, which involves interactions between instances of the same action, and externalities, which involve feedback across different actions.

In this lecture, we have four goals. First, to show how a combination of positive feedback and negative externalities produces path dependence. Second, to show how diversity produces tipping in systems with positive feedback. Third, to show how diversity produces stability in systems with negative feedback. Fourth, to show how interdependent actions can be written as a combination of feedback and externalities.

The keyboards that most of us use to type are known as QWERTY keyboards. How did the QWERTY format come to be? The QWERTY keyboard was designed to limit the likelihood of typewriter jams, and it took over the market because it created four distinct positive feedbacks. First, there was the scale of its production. Second, once you have learned to type on a QWERTY, it is easier to keep typing on one. Third, typing instruction manuals used the QWERTY design. And fourth, standardization enables resources to be shared.

The QWERTY also created negative externalities on other keyboard designs. It was not the initial state of the world that mattered for the dominance of QWERTY keyboards; it was the first few steps along the path. We refer to this as path dependence. Path-dependent processes are not predictable, a priori. The unpredictability of path-dependent processes does not stem from huge amounts of randomness; on the contrary, it depends on actions along the path.

Actions that create positive feedback produce more of the same actions. In contrast, actions that create negative feedback produce less of the same actions.

Let's now turn to our second goal—understanding how diversity plus positive feedback produce tipping. Let's model a system of 101 people fleeing a mall and see if this system can tip. We will consider two scenarios. In the first, everyone will have the same threshold, so only if the common threshold is one does one person leaving cause everyone to leave at once. If we add threshold diversity by assigning a different threshold to each person, the scenario has a tip. In complex systems, we often find that the tail (of the distribution of thresholds) wags the dog: The agents whose thresholds lie at the extremes have a large effect on the outcomes. This can also explain sorting. Thomas Schelling constructed one of the first agent-based models to explain how sorting occurs, and we can draw three lessons from Schelling's tipping model. We get segregation at the macro level even with tolerant individuals. Systems can tip; tipping goes in one direction.

We now turn to negative feedback, which tends to stabilize systems. Imagine a lake in which all of the species fix nitrogen and phosphorus levels so that the lake stays clean. Suppose we add some nitrogen to the lake. If the amount of nitrogen is small, the lake should handle it without much problem. We may be able to continue adding nitrogen and see no effect, until at some point the lake suddenly becomes eutrophic.

To see how this works, we will look at two models: an old-fashioned thermostat and a model of a beehive. The thermostat model demonstrates negative feedback because the thermostat does not perfectly stabilize the system. In the bee model, we see that genetically similar bees create fluctuations, while genetically diverse bees create stability. Additionally, in the bee model, suppose that the temperature outside gets to 120°F, and the hive temperature equals the outside temperature. We can think of this as a phase transition. The 120°F mark is a critical threshold, which is the tipping point.

To show that any interdependency can be written as a combination of feedback and externalities, let's step way back in our narrative. When we write a complex systems model, we are capturing the negative and positive feedbacks. Similarly, when we look at the effects on other actions, these either become more likely (a positive externality) or less likely (a negative externality). This sounds a lot like systems dynamics, but systems dynamics models differ from complex systems models in two important ways. Systems dynamics models do not include heterogeneity. Systems dynamics models do not include place. Does this mean that models that look at aggregates, like systems dynamics models, are not good models? Hardly. Understanding operates at many levels. When we move from aggregate-level thinking to agent-level thinking, we move from the world of systems dynamics to the world of complex systems. ■

Suggested Reading

Ball, *Critical Mass*.

Gladwell, *The Tipping Point*.

Page, "Path Dependence."

Schelling, *Micromotives and Macrobehavior*.

1. Teams must maintain an even keel. What types of feedback are necessary for stability in mood? What behaviors might produce these types of feedback?

2. Think about your own preferences about how you would like your neighbors to be. If everyone had the same preferences as you, what would residential patterns look like?

The Sand Pile—Self-Organized Criticality
Lecture 10

Complex systems often produce events whose distribution is not the traditional bell curve. One reason for that is that events are not independent; they are connected.

In this lecture, we learn the self-organized criticality theory, which explains why complex systems produce large events, like the Hatfield Airport incident. A system self-organizes if the aggregation of individual actions produces an organized pattern at the macro level. A system is said to be critical if small events trigger large cascades. Therefore, self-organized criticality implies that systems self-organize so that what emerges is critical—it can produce big events.

This lecture has four parts. First, we distinguish between normal distributions and long-tailed distributions. Second, we describe a simple random-walk model that produces a power-law distribution. Third, we discuss a model constructed by Per Bak called the sandpile model. In the final part, we will introduce a tension between complex systems thinking and optimization thinking.

First, we have normal and long-tailed distribution. Most of us are familiar with what is called the Gaussian or normal distribution: the bell curve. It is high in the middle and gradually tails off in each direction. The central limit theorem states that if we take the sum or the average of a bunch of independent random events, the result will be a bell curve. The fact that most things are normally distributed is crucial to the healthy functioning of a free and open society. In some cases, however, distribution is not normal. If we look at the distribution of sizes of wars, using deaths as a measure, we would see that most wars are very small, but every once in a while we get a huge war with many deaths. If you plot this data, you do not get a bell curve; you get a power law. Most of the events are small (this is the tall part), but huge events are possible (this is the long, flat part). Not all long-tailed distributions are power laws. Event sizes follow a power law if the probability of an event of size x is proportional to x raised to some negative power. Why and when do we not see a bell curve and instead see a power law?

Let's begin with a classic model that produces a power law distribution. Suppose we play the game called coin flipping. If we keep track of my winnings and they go 0, +1, +2, +1, +2, +1, 0, mathematicians call this a random walk. If we played the game a few million times, we could keep track of the distribution of the number of flips it took me to get back to 0.

Mathematicians call these return times. The distribution of return times for a random walk is a power law. This model appears to explain the distribution of the sizes of glacial lakes.

We need a model better suited to explaining wars, crashes, jams, and overruns. A candidate is Per Bak's sandpile model of self-organized criticality. Imagine a square table where individual grains of sand are sequentially dropped from above. These grains of sand accumulate until a pile begins to form. At some point, when an additional grain is added, the pile begins to collapse and some grains of sand topple from the table to the floor. If we count the grains of sand that hit the floor, we would find that most of the time only a grain or two topples the pile, but also that the avalanches are sometimes huge. It can be shown that the distribution of avalanche sizes follows a power law. Why might this and not the random walk model be a good model for explaining wars, traffic, and cost overruns?

Let's construct an even more stylized version of the sandpile model to see why. Assume the following rule: If at any time four bridge players find themselves in a square, they immediately leave the square, each one heading in a different direction. Like the sandpile model, this model self-organizes to a critical state because it starts producing cascades that follow a power-law distribution. The sandpile model and the bridge-player model produce a basic intuition that some systems can self-organize into critical states in which small events can trigger large cascades. How does this help us? First, it enables us to make better sense of the world. Second, as the world becomes more connected and more interdependent, we may be more likely to see large events. Third, the fact that we can build models may enable us to predict big events and in some cases prevent big events from occurring. Let me give three examples. First, we could stop those long tails caused by traffic jams if we could limit access to the right roads. Second, events like the Hatfield Airport incident could be prevented if connectedness is reduced (i.e., if security developed procedures to seal off portions of the airport very quickly). Finally, in the case of world wars, one good way to stop a cascade is to alleviate tension. The same goes for earthquakes. Central to our entire analysis is that the distribution of outcomes—the large events—depends on the complexity of the system. This idea that unpredictable events are not random but are the output of complexity represents a fundamental shift in perspective. ■

Suggested Reading

Anderson, *The Long Tail*.

Bak, *How Nature Works*.

Miller and Page, *Complex Adaptive Systems*.

Newman, "Power Laws, Pareto Distributions, and Zipf's Law."

Questions to Consider

1. How might a relationship between two partners self-organize into a critical state?

2. When might we want lots of small events and the rare big event and not a normal distribution of event sizes?

Complexity versus Uncertainty
Lecture 11

We focus on the difference between thinking of events as random and thinking of them as the output of a complex system and why this distinction matters.

What is the difference between thinking of events as random and thinking of them as the output of a complex system? The New York Stock Exchange is a complex adaptive system, and it produces large events. These large events are mostly crashes, but there have also been days in which the market has made extraordinary gains. We can think of these fluctuations in either of two ways. We can think of them as random events. We can think of them as outcomes of complex systems. In this lecture, we focus on why this distinction matters.

Our analysis consists of three parts. Examining the sources of randomness, including complexity. Examining the difference between randomness that comes from complexity and other sorts of randomness. Examining how the way we think about interventions changes when we take up a complex systems perspective.

Where does randomness come from? There are three standard accounts of the source of randomness. Randomness can be engineered. Randomness can be caused by another randomness. Randomness can be a fundamental property. Complexity theory offers a fourth possible explanation: interdependent rules. Recall our discussion of cellular automaton models, where we considered strings of holiday lights and each light followed a rule. If we begin with just one light, the light's sequences of ons and offs, over time, will appear random, and we would not be able to predict with any accuracy what the next state would be. A simple cellular automaton rule produces randomness, and what we see as fundamental randomness may be the result of simple interacting rules.

This insight—that complexity produces what might appear to be random outcomes—leads us to our second point: how randomness that comes from complexity differs from other sorts of randomness. First the (obvious) intuition. Think back to our lecture on diversity, where we talked about how complex systems adapt. This implies that we have no guarantee that the distribution of outcomes in the future will be identical to the distribution of outcomes today. In the formal language of statistics, this is referred to as nonstationarity. A process in which the distribution of outcomes does not change, on the other hand, is said to have stationarity.

Where does randomness come from? There are three standard accounts of the source of randomness. ... Complexity theory offers a fourth possible explanation: interdependent rules.

Why is the distinction between stationarity and nonstationarity so important? Consider the case of Long-Term Capital Management, a hedge fund that failed and failed big due to unexpected market complexity. For another example of how stationary thinking in a complex world leads to tragedy, we need look no further than the 2008 home mortgage crisis. The author and decision theorist Nassim Taleb refers to large, hard-to-predict events such as these as black swans.

This leads us to our third point, which is the idea that complexity not only creates randomness but also has implications for how we think about interventions. Suppose we have developed a potential cure for high blood pressure that might lower blood pressure by 10 percent in approximately 30 percent of patients, compared to a placebo that lowers blood pressure by 10 percent in only 5 percent of patients.

Let's contrast three views of the drug efficacy data. We could adopt a uncertainty mind-set and think of the success of our elixir as a random event. Doctors take a conditional probability approach: They think of the outcome as conditional on the patient. Finally, we can take a complex systems view of the intervention. If we focus on just two implications of complexity thinking, even if the elixir works, we have no guarantee that it will continue to work in the future. On the other hand, if something doesn't work, that doesn't mean it won't work the next time.

We have talked a lot in these lectures about how much complexity there is in the world. Economies, political systems, social networks, ecologies, and even our brains can be thought of as complex. The outcomes of those complex systems fluctuate. It may be easier to think of those fluctuations as random events, but as we have seen in this lecture, if we ignore the complexity that underlies the fluctuations, we can produce large events and we can perform improper interventions. ■

Suggested Reading

Holland, *Adaptation in Natural and Artificial Systems*.

Questions to Consider

1. Do your financial advisors give you advice based on a stationary model of randomness or a nonstationary model? If the former, are you concerned?

2. Even though we cannot predict the future, use ideas from all of the lectures to explain why we might be able to predict the distribution of future events.

Harnessing Complexity
Lecture 12

If a system is complex, can we intervene productively? Can we reduce complexity? Would we want to?

Why would someone want to learn about complex systems? I came up with two reasons, which are also the reasons why I continue my own research into complex systems. Complex systems are inherently interesting, producers of amazing novelty, and not clean and simple, which makes them a lively playground for the mind. Complex systems are where the action is. The fundamental challenges of our time are all complex.

In the first 11 lectures, we focused primarily on learning the basics of complex systems. In this last lecture, we turn to the takeaways. What have we learned from this brief foray into the study of complex systems? How can it help us choose better courses of action, or even to make sense of the complex world around us? I think of this last lecture exploring the space between "lion taming" and "poking the tiger with a stick." We cannot hope to control complex systems through interventions. At best, we might learn to harness and respect complexity.

We will begin by describing a noncomplex system of making choices that is known as decision theory. This will provide a benchmark against which to compare the lessons we learn from complex systems. The canonical decision theory model of how to make choices can be described in a few steps. The first step is to determine a set of options. The second step is to determine the payoff of each option in each state of the world. The third step is to compute the probability of each state of the world. Once you have written down all of the options, all of the possible states, and the payoffs of every option in every state, then you can make a rational choice.

This canonical decision-making model works great if, for example, you want to decide which computer to buy, but it is not a very useful model for determining what to do in a complex system. Let me give four big reasons. The standard decision-making model does not take into account the behavior of other interested actors. The standard decision-making model translates complexity into uncertainty. The standard decision-making model is all exploitation. The standard decision-making model focuses on a single outcome, not on system properties. Therefore, the model takes no account of what the system might be like as a result of your action.

The first step toward effective action in a complex world is recognition. Not everything is complex. Some systems are linear and predictable, though these are not the same thing. An effect is linear if we get a straight line when we plot it. An effect is predictable if we know what will happen. An effect can be linear and predictable or linear and unpredictable. An effect can also be nonlinear but predictable. Finally, we can have nonlinear effects that are unpredictable. Complex systems often produce these sorts of effects.

Systems that are not complex can be controlled. We can figure out what to do best. Situations that are complex require an awareness of the parts that make them complex so that you can keep an eye on key attributes. Once complexity has been recognized, we at least have the hope of harnessing it, of taming the lion.

Let's think about how we might harness complexity to do good. Our first step will be to think in terms of the attributes of choice

Ralph Waldo Emerson wrote, "As soon as there is life, there is danger."

variables or levers, which we can choose to increase diversity or decrease interdependencies. Let's start with diversity, where our first insight is to encourage diversity—but not too much. Without some source of diversity, selection will drive systems toward pure exploitation, which can be dangerous. Diversity also prevents error. Another bit of advice is to keep an eye on the tails. Next, let's think about selection mechanisms as a lever, where our second insight is to be careful how you define goals and incentives. Then let's consider interdependencies, where our third insight is to not become so obsessed with making small efficiency improvements that you push a system toward a critical state. Last but not least, let's look at connections, where our fourth insight is to search for potentially synergistic links and cut those that limit responsiveness.

These lessons are easier said than done, but notice the coherence among them. Synergistic links exploit diversity and positive interdependencies. Selection tempers diversity to help balance exploration and exploitation. Pulling back on efficiency a bit to allow some slack not only ensures robustness, it promotes greater innovation by allowing diversity.

Let's do an empirical test to see what types of organizations prove robust. Let's look at organizations that have been around for more than 500 years; this group includes more than 40 universities and around 125 or so businesses. They show that a little slack is a good thing, if you want robustness. In Jenna Bednar's book *The Robust Federation*, she makes the point that robust federated governments also need space for a little slippage.

Complex systems are inherently interesting, producers of amazing novelty, and not clean and simple, which makes them a lively playground for the mind.

Many of the core insights we have discussed in this lecture seem straightforward, but let's just recognize how they depart from the standard idea of command-and-control optimization. If you take a command-and-control optimization approach, you set incentives with only outcomes in mind. Command-and-control optimization is not wrong, but it is a poor approach if we are hoping to thrive in a complex world. Our goal should be to push our understanding of these systems. Only through understanding can we move from a position of poking the tiger with a stick to one where we are taming the lion. ∎

Suggested Reading

Axelrod and Cohen, *Harnessing Complexity*.

Questions to Consider

1. Suppose you intervene in a complex system by adjusting the diversity level. How might you know that, rather than taming the lion, you have just poked the tiger with a stick?

2. Given what you have learned about complex systems, do you believe that the success of any one person depends more on their individual attributes or on context—on where that person happens to be situated?

Glossary

adaptation: A change in behavior or actions in response to a payoff or fitness function.

agent-based model: A computer model of a complex system that builds from individual agents.

complex adaptive system: A collection of adaptive, diverse, connected entities with interdependent actions.

complicated. A system of connected, diverse, interdependent parts that are not adaptive.

dancing landscapes: Fitness or payoff landscapes that are coupled so that when one entity changes, its action causes the other entity's landscape to shift.

diversity: Differences in the number of types of entities.

emergence: A higher-level phenomenon that arises from the micro-level interactions in a complex system. Emergence can be weak (explicable) or strong (unexplained). Consciousness, for example, is an instance of strong emergence.

explore/exploit: The trade-off between searching for better solutions and taking advantage of what is known.

externality: When an action by one entity influences the payoff or fitness of the actions of another agent. This creates dancing landscapes.

interaction: Effects between the multiple actions of a single entity. These are the cause of rugged landscapes.

interdependence: The influence of one entity's action on the behavior, payoff, or fitness of another entity.

long-tailed distribution: A distribution such as a power law in which most event sizes are small but some are very large.

network: A collection of nodes and links, or connections between those nodes.

nonstationary process: A process in which the probability of events changes over time.

normal distribution: The familiar bell-curve distribution in which most likely event sizes are near the mean.

phase transition: An abrupt change in the macro-level properties of a system.

positive and negative feedbacks: A situation in which an action creates more (positive) or less (negative) of the same action.

power-law network: A network in which the distribution of links fits a model of a type of long-tailed distribution.

robustness: The ability of a complex system to maintain functionality given a disturbance.

rugged landscape: A graphical representation of a difficult problem in which the value of a potential solution is represented as an elevation.

selection: A process through which less fit or lower-performing entities are removed from the population.

self-organization: A form of emergence in which the entities create a pattern or structure from the bottom-up, such as schooling fish.

self-organized criticality: A phenomenon in which interaction agents self-organize into states that can produce large events.

simulated annealing: A search algorithm in which the probability of making an error decreases over time.

small-world network: A network in which the nodes are people and the people have local friends and a few random friends.

tipping point: A configuration in a complex system in which a sequence of events can push the system into a new macro state.

variance: A difference in the value of an attribute.

Bibliography

Anderson, Chris. *The Long Tail: Why the Future of Business is Selling Less of More*. New York: Hyperion, 2006. Anderson describes how new technologies allow for more small niche markets. His long tails are the opposite of the long tails that we discuss in power laws. In power laws, the long tails represent large events. In Anderson's model, the long tail represents many small events.

Anderson, Phillip. "More is Different." *Science* 177 (August 4, 1972): 393–396. Though published in a scientific journal by a Nobel laureate in physics, this paper is accessible and provides one of the earliest and most coherent descriptions of emergence. It is considered one of the founding papers of complex systems theory.

Axelrod, Robert. *The Complexity of Cooperation: Agent-Based Models of Competition and Collaboration*. Princeton, NJ: Princeton University Press, 1997. This book provides some examples of complexity applied to social science problems such as cooperation and the formation of culture. It is an ideal book for someone interested in how social scientists put ideas from complex systems to work by using agent-based models.

Axelrod, Robert, and Michael Cohen. *Harnessing Complexity: Organizational Implications of a Scientific Frontier*. New York: Basic Books, 2001. This book provides the backbone for the final lecture in which I discuss how to harness complexity. Axelrod and Cohen are central figures in complex systems study, and they wrote this book for business people and policy makers to help them understand how to harness the power of complexity.

Bak, Per. *How Nature Works: The Science of Self-Organized Criticality*. 1st ed. New York: Springer, 1996. Here Bak describes his sand-pile model of self-organized criticality in accessible prose. He then shows how the model can be applied to a variety of settings. It is a wonderful book, bursting with Bak's passion for his ideas. This book cannot be described as understated!

Ball, Philip. *Critical Mass: How One Thing Leads to Another.* 1st ed. New York: Farrar, Straus and Giroux, 2004. Ball's book is a wonderful follow-up to Melanie Mitchell's book on complexity. Ball digs much deeper into the physics of complex systems and argues that many of the new ideas of complex systems borrow from existing ideas in physics. He provides a wonderful analysis of phase transitions.

Bednar, Jenna. *The Robust Federation: Principles of Design.* New York: Cambridge University Press, 2008. Most formal models of institutions in social science focus on efficiency: The best institutions are the most efficient. Bednar first shows that efficiency may be impossible in federations owing to imperfect monitoring. She goes on to show that the inherent slippages in a federal arrangement, far from being detrimental, actually enhance robustness by allowing for experimentation and innovation. Her theory also touches on the need for coverage and redundancy in institutional design. All in all, a deep, thoughtful book.

Beinhocker, Eric. *Origin of Wealth: Evolution, Complexity, and the Radical Remaking of Economics.* Cambridge, MA: Harvard University Press, 2007. Written by a leading business consultant and frequent visitor to the Santa Fe Institute, this book describes how complex systems ideas can be used to understand core features of the economy. The book challenges the standard economics orthodoxy.

Epstein, Joshua. *Generative Social Science: Studies in Agent-Based Computational Modeling.* Princeton, NJ: Princeton University Press, 2007. This book contains a collection of articles that rely on agent-based models. Epstein describes how bottom-up agent-based models can be thought of as generative. The book includes both a cogent philosophical contrast between generating an outcome and proving the existence of such an outcome and a wealth of examples that demonstrate the difference.

———. *Growing Artificial Societies: Social Science from the Bottom Up.* Cambridge, MA: MIT Press, 1996. This book describes many of the key concepts in complex systems by using an elaborate agent-based model called Sugarscape. In this model, the agents demonstrate the difference between bottom-up and top-down social science.

Gladwell, Malcolm. *The Tipping Point: How Little Things Can Make a Big Difference*. 1st ed. New York: Little, Brown and Company, 2000. Gladwell shows how very minor adjustments can lead to major impacts in everyday life. This is written for a nontechnical audience; as a result, it is a quick, fun read. Gladwell touches on many of the ideas discussed in the lectures: tipping points, networks, and positive feedbacks among them.

Holland, John. *Adaptation in Natural and Artificial Systems: An Introductory Analysis with Applications to Biology, Control, and Artificial Intelligence.* Cambridge, MA: MIT Press, 1992. This book initiated study in the field of complex adaptive systems. It provides the first full description of genetic algorithms and classifiers and of how systems that adapt can solve problems. This book requires substantial mathematical sophistication on the part of the reader.

———. *Emergence: From Chaos To Order*. New York: Basic Books, 1999. Holland demonstrates that the "emergence" of order from chaos has much to teach us about life, mind, and organizations. This book is written for a more general audience and is a fun, lively read, bursting with ideas. It provides an excellent description of lever points.

———. *Hidden Order: How Adaptation Builds Complexity*. Reading, MA: Helix Books, 1996. Written by one of the founders of complexity theory, this book describes the basic concepts of the theory for a more general audience. Unlike many books on complexity, this book is low on hype and high on substance. For those who want a book with lots of substance (but no equations), this is an ideal choice.

Jackson, Matthew. *Social and Economic Networks*. Princeton, NJ: Princeton University Press, 2008. Jackson's book offers a comprehensive introduction to social and economic networks. Primarily written as a textbook for graduate students in economics, it contains a clear, concise introduction to the theoretical study of networks. Each chapter includes exercises to aid network analysis comprehension.

Kauffman, Stuart. *At Home in the Universe: The Search for Laws of Self Organization and Complexity*. New York: Oxford University Press, 1996. This book focuses on the origins of complexity and self-organization in a biological system. Written for the general science reader, it relies on complex systems ideas to explain how life may have come into being through emergence.

Miller, John, and Scott Page. *Complex Adaptive Systems: An Introduction to Computational Models of Social Life*. Princeton, NJ: Princeton University Press, 2007. This book provides an intermediate-level introduction to complex adaptive systems. It provides formal versions of many of the models discussed in the course and an introduction to agent-based modeling. This book is geared toward the interested general reader with a slight social science bent.

Mitchell, Melanie. *Complexity: A Guided Tour*. New York: Oxford University Press, 2009. An excellent introduction to the field of complex systems written by a leading computer scientist and complex systems scholar. The book draws examples from biology, computer science, and social science. As far as introductions to complex systems go, this is one of the best.

———. *An Introduction to Genetic Algorithms*. Cambridge, MA: MIT Press, 1998. Genetic algorithms, a computer search algorithm introduced by John Holland, encode potential solutions as strings and then use crossover, mutation, and selection to breed new solutions. In this book, Mitchell provides an introduction to genetic algorithms and explains how they can identify and combine partial solutions. This is a great book for anyone interested in learning more about how computer algorithms work.

Newman, Mark. "Power Laws, Pareto Distributions and Zipf's Law." *Contemporary Physics* 46 (September, 2005): 323–351. In this technical academic paper, Newman provides some of the empirical evidence and theories for the existence of power-law forms. This paper requires advanced training in mathematics to understand fully. Nevertheless, as a resource for what might cause power laws, it is unsurpassed.

Newman, Mark, Albert-Lászól Barabasi, and Duncan J. Watts. *The Structure and Dynamics of Networks*. Princeton, NJ: Princeton University Press, 2006. This book provides an overview of the latest breakthroughs in network theory. The book is organized into four sections. It discusses some of the important historical research, the network's empirical side, and the foundational modeling ideas and explores the relationship between network structure and system dynamics.

Page, Scott E. *The Difference: How the Power of Diversity Creates Better Groups, Firms, Schools, and Societies*. Princeton, NJ: Princeton University Press, 2007. This book demonstrates the value of diversity by using models from complex systems. The book shows how rugged landscapes depend on a person's perspective and how collections of bounded agents can produce diverse solutions to problems and make accurate predictions.

———. "Path Dependence." *Quarterly Journal of Political Science* 1 (January 1, 2006): 87–115. In this academic paper, I provide an overview of the causes and types of path dependence. I use a simple model of urns containing two colors of balls to draw distinctions between the types of path dependence. The paper contains a more complete telling of the QWERTY keyboard example.

Raymond, Eric S. *The Cathedral and the Bazaar: Musings on Linux and Open Source by an Accidental Revolutionary*. 1st ed. Sebastopol, CA: O'Reilly, 1999. An excellent book on the difference between top-down organizational structures (the cathedral) and the bottom-up, open-source approach (the bazaar). Raymond's book challenges how many think about organizations and efficiency.

Resnick, Mitchel. *Turtles, Termites, and Traffic Jams: Explorations in Massively Parallel Microworlds*. Cambridge, MA: MIT Press, 1994. Resnick developed a computer program called StarLogo, which was the predecessor to NetLogo, a common agent-based modeling platform. StarLogo was written for younger people to learn to construct agent-based models. Resnick shows how to use StarLogo and agent-based models to produce a variety of phenomena.

Bibliography

Schelling, Thomas. *Micromotives and Macrobehavior*. 1st ed. New York: W. W. Norton, 1978. This book contains the tipping model of segregation discussed in this course. That model is one of many treasures in this tour de force, a book that more than any other was responsible for Schelling winning the Nobel Prize. Many of the phenomena Schelling describes would now be called emergent, though at the time that word was not used in conjunction with the sort of models he describes.

Waldrop, Mitchell. *Complexity: The Emerging Science at the Edge of Order and Chaos*. New York: Simon and Schuster, 1992. This book put the idea of complexity in the public consciousness. It offers up a journalistic account of the history of complex systems research at the Santa Fe Institute. Waldrop describes the big ideas of complex systems through the eyes of the scientists that developed them. It is written as a popular science book that can be read by anyone.

Watts, Duncan. *Six Degrees of Separation: The Science of a Connected Age*. New York: W. W. Norton, 2004. A great introduction to the science of networks. Watts mixes captivating examples with deep theory. The book describes how different network structures exhibit different functionalities, including the famous six degrees of separation.

—————. *Six Degrees: The Science of a Connected Age*. New York: W. W. Norton, 2003. This is perhaps the best mass-audience book on networks. Watts writes with clarity and rigor about small-worlds networks, network robustness, and network formation. He peppers his analysis with lively examples.

Weiner, Jonathan. *The Beak of the Finch: A Story of Evolution in Our Time*. New York: Vintage, 1995. This book provides a wonderful description of the work of two biologists who go to the Galapagos and study Darwin's finches. They find that evolution occurs more rapidly than Darwin thought. This book won a Pulitzer Prize.

West, Geoffrey. *Scaling Laws in Biology and Other Complex Systems*. Google Tech Talks, 2007; 54 min., 30 sec.; streaming video, http://video.google.com/videoplay?docid=7108406426776765294. This is a Google TechTalk that examines how universal scaling laws follow from fundamental principles and lead to a general quantitative theory that captures essential features of many diverse biological systems. The talk is somewhat technical but provides a powerful demonstration of the fan-out nature of complex systems.

Notes

Notes

Notes

Notes